A Day at PreSchool

The Elizabeth Books

A Day at PreSchool
A Fun Place to Play with New Friends
A picture book to read to kids entering preschool

Elizabeth at School
A Safe Place to Learn
A picture book for ages 6 – 8

Elizabeth in Paris
Traveling with My Mom, the Artist
A picture book for ages 6 – 8

The Flood
The Dangerous Exploits of Three Girls, a Cat and a Boat
A chapter book for ages 9 – 12

The Elizabeth Books

A Day at PreSchool

A Fun Place to Play with New Friends

Written and Illustrated
by Wendy Bartlett

Kensington Hill Books
Berkeley, California

These drawings were done by Wendy Bartlett at the U.C. Berkeley Childcare Center.

Kensington Hill Books
Berkeley, California

kensingtonhillbooks.com

Ordering Information:
Quantity sales. Special discounts are available on quantity purchases by schools, associations, and others. For details, contact the publisher via the Contact page on the above website.

A Day at PreSchool: A Fun Place to Play with New Friends / Wendy Bartlett —2nd ed.
ISBN 978-1-9449070-2-0 print
ISBN 978-1-9449070-3-7 ebook

This book is dedicated
to Bertie and Sidney

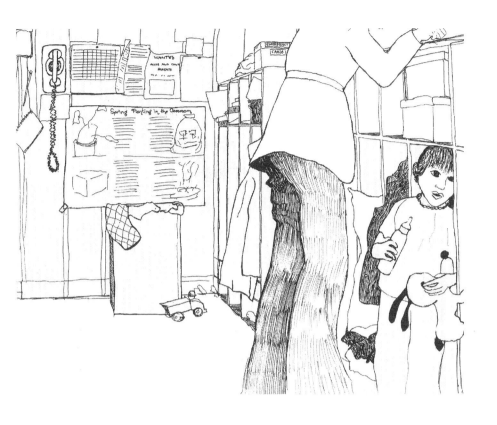

Some days when I come to our preschool

My mom signs me in and I'm sad.

Sometimes I am scared and I miss her,

And when she comes back I am glad.

Our hands are getting sticky,

But we don't care that much.

The glue gets on our paper,

And on everything we touch.

Our teacher here is Joe.

He teaches everything.

The nicest man we know.

He even helps us sing.

We're matching pretty pictures

To pictures on the card.

Sometimes we can match them

And sometimes it is hard.

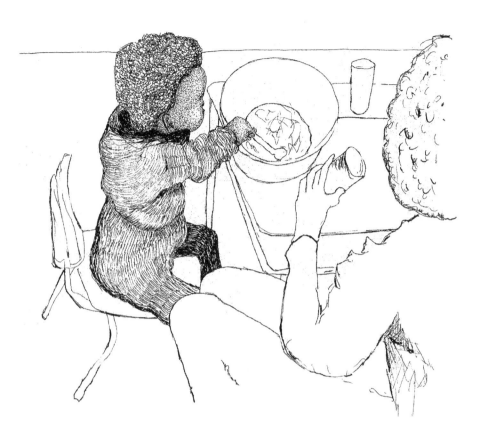

I measure out the flour,

And pour the water in.

He holds tight to the wooden spoon,

And stirs it again and again.

It's time again for snack-time.

We wash our hands and then,

We find our chair and table,

And sit down by a friend.

Crackers and fruit and milk and juice,

And raisins and carrots and cheese.

Sometimes we spill the juice from our cup,

And it gets all over our knees.

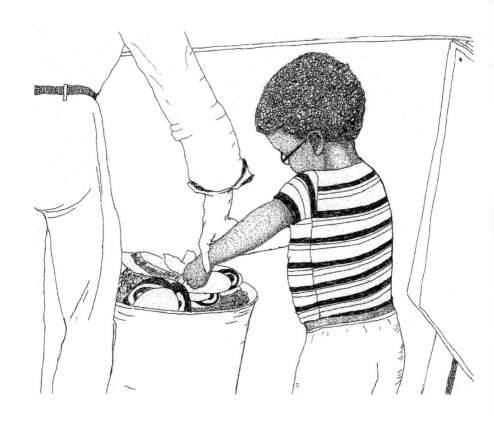

The teacher tries to help Rob

When he throws his plate away.

Teacher thinks the food will spill.

"I can do it myself, today."

After I eat I like to play,

Perhaps I'll go for a ride.

Bouncing along, up and down,

Makes me feel funny inside.

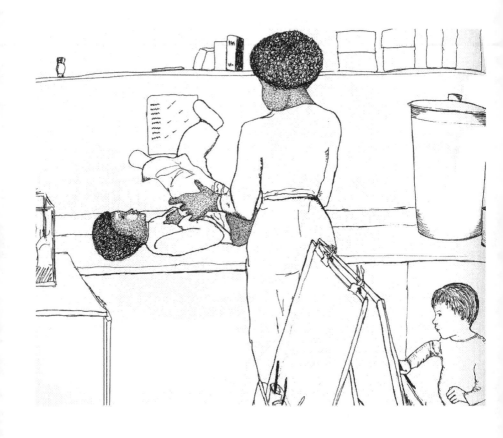

It looks like the changing table to me,

And the woman looks just like a mother.

The boy is painting a picture,

Like no other, no other, no other.

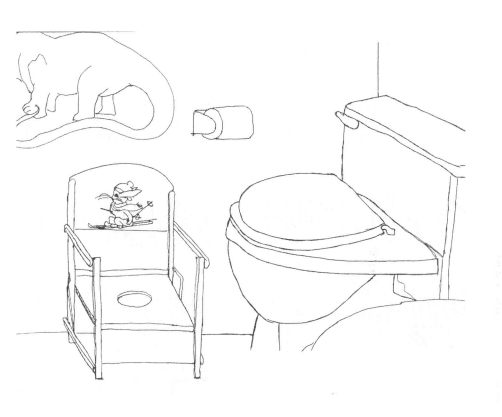

Each day we are growing bigger,

And some of us go potty here.

When we're learning we go on the little one.

When we're bigger we go over there.

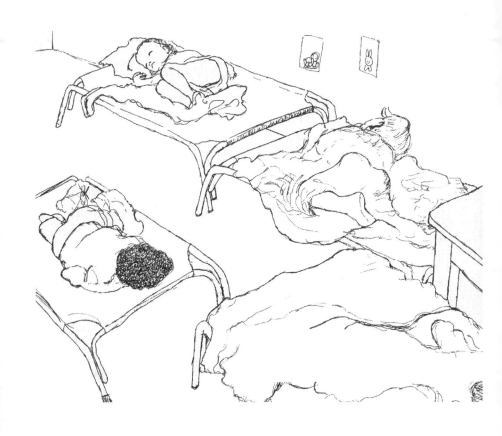

We've eaten and lunchtime is over,

And some of us like to lie down.

Some children are sleeping and dreaming,

So we'd better not make a sound.

Michael looks warm and cozy,

And far off in another land.

Dreaming of beaches and birthdays
and boats,

And castles made of sand.

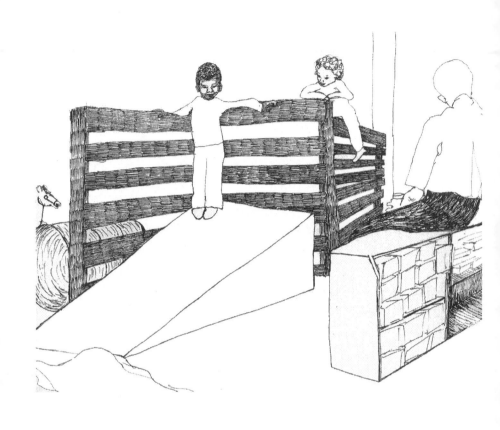

Running up and sliding down,

Or else just standing there.

On top it is a fire engine,

Stop it if you dare.

This is the corner where we play house,

We keep all the dolls in the bed.

Sometimes we throw them all over the floor,

And climb in ourselves instead.

Please push us higher and higher, we beg,

Way up in the sky we go.

We feel like birds just learning to fly,

We can see all the world below.

Sounds from the chords of a lovely guitar

Echo like songs that she sings.

When he grows up he will play one, too,

And make magical music with strings.

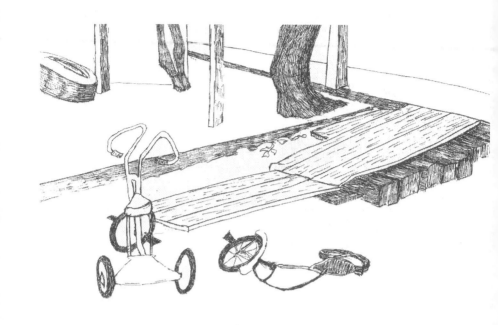

Bikes and trikes are lots of fun,

And maybe we'll fall down.

It happens when we're going fast,

Or going round and round.

One day he felt very angry,

And wouldn't get out of the way.

That was just where he wanted to stand,

And he doesn't care what they say.

Bang, bang, bang, bang, bang, bang, bang.

OW! I hit my thumb!

I cry and then I start again,

For hammering is fun!

Ch-ka, ch-ka, ch-ka, ch-ka,

Back and forth we go.

Back and forth, back and forth,

Sawing's work, you know.

Peek-a-boo, I see you,

Behind that big old box.

The other kid is on his horse,

Jumping over rocks.

One day we took a trip to see

A lovely little farm.

They have an animal center there,

Where they are safe from harm.

Grownups voices sound the best,

When reading us a book.

We like to watch the pictures,

And we need time to look.

Goodbye, goodbye, my guinea pig,

It's time for me to go.

Don't cry, I'm coming back again,

I love you still, you know.

Wee Willie Winkie
A Fingerplay Rhyme

Wee Willie Winkie

Runs through the town

Upstairs
and downstairs

In his nightgown

Rapping
at the window

Crying at the lock

Are the children in their beds?

For now it's eight o'clock.

Acknowledgements

As always, the first acknowledgement goes to my wonderful daughter, Elizabeth Stark (BookWritingWorld.com), a great writer and teacher who has guided me every step of my journey with her wise feedback. Nanou Matteson, who was once a part of my writers' group and also one of my wonderful teachers, deserves a hearty thanks. My writers' group is, of course, my mainstay and many thanks go to those who used to be in it, and those who remain to this day: Marilynn Rowland, Sarita Berg, Dean Curtis, Ruth Hanham, Doris Fine, Elizabeth Greene, Joyce Scott, Carol Nyhoff, Karen Bird and others. Thanks go to the many friends who helped me feel okay with the drawings, especially my brother, Tom Gilb, who said I was the illustrator I was looking for.

I would like to thank my friends and advisers at the Bay Area Independent Publishers Association, especially Lorna Johnson, who completed the inside graphics, and Val Sherer for starting the layout process and for general good advice.

Special thanks to Ruth Schwartz for getting this to the final stages and making it real!

I would like to thank and acknowledge all the people who run The San Francisco Writers Conference, and, in particular, Michael Larsen, Elizabeth Pomada, and Laurie McLean, for the many ways they have changed my life as I wrote and volunteered for many years since 2008.

Thanks to all those of you who have read this book and written reviews, the author's gold, especially Leo and Charlie! And to Angie Powers for her amazing author photograph!

About the Author

Wendy Bartlett lived in England for thirteen years where she attended the Maria Grey College of Further Education and received her Teaching Certificate. There she majored in art and education, and then taught for two years at a London primary school. Wendy has a B.A. from U.C. Berkeley  in Art History, and has a California Teaching Credential. She worked as a pre-school teacher at the U.C. Berkeley Childcare Center for five years, and occasionally taught children of all ages in Oakland. She has a daughter, Elizabeth Stark, who is a hero in her series, *The Elizabeth Books,* inspired by Elizabeth's childhood.

kensingtonhillbooks.com

Made in the USA
Middletown, DE
10 September 2021